QUINTET

for 2 Violins, 2 Violas and Violoncello
G minor/g-Moll/Sol mineur
K 516
Edited by/Herausgegeben von
Rudolf Gerber

Ernst Eulenburg Ltd

London · Mainz · Madrid · New York · Paris · Tokyo · Toronto · Zürich

I. Allegro 1

II. MENUETTO. Allegretto 18

III. Adagio ma non troppo 22

IV. Adagio—Allegro 29

MOZART — QUINTET G MINOR K.-V. № 516

In Mozart's output of chamber-music the Quintets for stringed instruments are of far less importance than the String Quartets. Yet it is significant enough that his first String Quintet, written at the instigation of Michael Haydn and the Italian, Sammartini, in the year 1773 (Köchel Edition 174) underwent two settings, and that this first effort was not followed up by others, as was the case in some musical forms undertaken by him for the first time, such as the Quartet or Violin Concerto. The double setting also throws immediate light on the problem raised by this first offspring, namely, the conflict between the freedom of the *Divertimento* style and strict chamber-music form — the thoughtful, serious vein by which Mozart saw himself bound. And the reason why he did not further pursue this style lay probably in the perception that the string quintet, developed on *Divertimento* lines, was of little use and even perhaps inadaptable; another reason being the bare and simple fact that no demand existed for *ensemble* works of this character. When Mozart returned to the same form fourteen years later, both these considerations were of no object. He neither endeavoured to treat the String Quintet in the *Divertimento* fashion, nor did he

seek commissions and hope for possible sales. The two String Quintets in C major and G minor of the year 1787 are, in any case, works of an avowedly personal kind, which owe their existence to the artistic expression of a fundamental, spiritual impulse. And if the last two works in this form — the D major Quintet of the year 1790 and the E flat major Quintet of the year 1791 — were composed "at the urgent entreaties of a musical friend"[1]), that is quite different from "writing to order"[2]).

After the great expansion of power exhibited in Mozart's String Quartets, culminating in the masterpieces of the six works dedicated to Joseph Haydn, Mozart found an aesthestic outlet in the String Quintet as the strongest instrumental embodiment of the art of chamber-music rooted in his innermost being. He now suddenly caused surprise with two works, which, immediately following one another, remain to this day models of the form.

In the year 1787 — the year in which "Don Giovanni" was composed — he completed on April 19th and May 16th respectively the C major and the G minor Quintets (Köchel 515, 516); those two works which reflect completely the enormous expanse of expression exhibited in the later Mozart. Although

---

[1]) O. Jahn, Mozart, (1859), vol. 4, page 96.
[2]) The fact that Mozart took the String Quintet very seriously is proved by the various sketches he made for it (K.-V. 79—84 Appendix); their chronological order, however, cannot with safety be determined.

the C major Quintet displays a fundamental note of conciliation and happy freedom of spirit, it also reveals a certain sorrowful reserve of expression, which, in the first three movements, is depicted by sharply dramatic emphasis or by hesitant turns of phrase. The G minor Quintet is quite another matter. It is, "after the G minor Symphony, the most deeply-felt work of Mozart's in that key"; a composition "yielding, forcibly, a picture of bitter resignation, with striking effect". This work is "the exact opposite of the Piano Concertos; the production of a lonely soul, resolving the dark forces of fate without gaining mastery over them, in the Beethovian sense. He accepts and suffers all trials apportioned him as things immutable; and if, in the Finale, he rediscovers the joy of life, it must not be interpreted as a Beethovian victory following past struggles, but in the Mozartian sense, as one who, practically-minded, would co-ordinate the contrasts of reality".[1])

Works, less familiar than these two corner-stones of Quintet literature, but on that account no less important, are the two last String Quintets in D major (Köchel 593) of December 1790 and E flat major (Köchel 614) of April 1791. The latter, especially, in its general merriment of mood and occasional purely popular thematic invention recalls the earlier Mozart, the joyous intoxicated atmosphere of the "Magic Flute".

Together with these five String Quintets attention must be drawn to the arrangement of two Wind Serenades — the B flat major Serenade (Köchel 361)[2]), and, more especially, the C minor Serenade (Köchel 388).

Obviously, in such an arrangement for strings, many delicate tonal shades must be lost; this is particularly so in the B flat major work. On the other hand, in the C minor Serenade, Mozart was clearly imbued with the feeling that, here, chamber-music was in question — a chamber-work of the deepest meaning, fore-shadowing the G minor Quintet. Hence, in the arrangement for strings, this work should unhesitatingly be ranked on a level with the String Quintets.

The present edition of the G minor Quintet is founded on the autograph copy, in the possession of the Prussian State Library in Berlin. Deviations from editions generally accessible are confined mainly to marks of phrasing. Perusal of the original manuscript however—especially in the last movement—occasioned the rectification of several fanciful legato markings (bar 59, Viola I; bar 186, Violin II) which may prove not unimportant[3]).

Rudolf Gerber

---

[1]) H. Abert, Mozart, vol. 2, page 387.
[2]) Cf. Eulenburg Min.-Sc. No. 100.
[3]) See also in the first movement bars 60/61 in first Viola; bar 96 in 2nd Viola and bar 100 in Violin II.

MOZART, QUINTETT G MOLL K.-V. № 516

Im Kammermusikschaffen Mozarts treten die Quintette für Saiteninstrumente mit weit geringerer Betonung hervor als die Streichquartette. Ist es doch schon bezeichnend genug, daß sein erstes, durch Michael Haydn und den Italiener Sammartini angeregtes Streichquintett (K.-V. 174) vom Jahre 1733 in zwei Fassungen vorliegt, und daß diesem ersten Versuch keine weiteren folgten, wie dies bei andern, erstmals von ihm in Angriff genommenen Gattungen, dem Quartett oder dem Violinkonzert, der Fall war. Die doppelte Fassung beleuchtet auch bereits das Problematische dieses Erstlingswerkes, den Konflikt zwischen divertimentohafter Unbeschwertheit und kammermusikalischer Strenge, gedanklichem Ernst, in den sich Mozart gedrängt sah. Und die Gründe, weshalb er die Gattung nicht weiter verfolgte, lagen wohl in der Erkenntnis, daß das Saitenquintett zu divertimentohaften Gestaltungen ungebräuchlich und vielleicht auch wenig geeignet war, sowie überdies in der einfachen Tatsache, daß nach derartigen Ensemblewerken keine Nachfrage bestand. Als Mozart vierzehn Jahre später sich erneut der Gattung zuwandte, waren beide Bedenken gegenstandslos geworden. Weder kam er jetzt noch in Versuchung, mit dem Streichquintett divertimentohaft zu musizieren, noch fragte er nach Bestellung und „Absatzmöglichkeiten". Die beiden Streichquintette in

C dur und g moll aus dem Jahre 1787 jedenfalls sind Bekenntniswerke höchstpersönlicher Art. die der künstlerischen Darstellung eines elementaren inneren Dranges ihr Dasein verdanken. Und wenn er die beiden letzten Werke dieser Gattung, das D dur-Quintett vom Jahre 1790 und das Es dur-Quintett vom Jahre 1791 „auf eine sehr thätige Aneiferung eines Musikfreundes"[1] geschrieben haben soll, so ist das etwas anderes als „auf Bestellung geschrieben"[2].

Nach dem großen Reifeprozeß seines Streichquartettschaffens, der in den Meisterwerken der sechs Josef Haydn gewidmeten Quartette seinen ersten Niederschlag fand, war für Mozart innerlich die Bahn frei zum Streichquintett als der stärksten instrumentalen Verkörperung einer in seelischen Tiefen wurzelnden Kammerkunst. Jetzt überraschte er auch sogleich mit zwei Werken, die, unmittelbar nacheinander entstanden, Urbilder der Gattung geblieben sind bis auf den heutigen Tag. Im Jahr des „Don Giovanni", 1787, am 19. April und 16. Mai vollendete er das C dur- und das g moll-Quintett (K. V. 515, 516), jene beiden Werke, die den ungeheueren Spannungsreichtum des späten Mozart in vollkommener Weise widerspiegeln. Obwohl das C-dur-Quintett auf einen versöhnlichen und sinnenfreudigen Grundton gestimmt ist, lebt doch schon in ihm eine gewisse schmerzliche Verhalten-

[1] O. Jahn, Mozart (1859), 4. Bd. S. 96.
[2] Daß sich Mozart um das Streichquintett ernsthaft bemüht hat, beweisen die verschiedenen Skizzen K.-V. 79—84 Anhang, deren zeitliche Einordnung jedoch nicht mit Sicherheit vorgenommen werden kann.

heit des Ausdrucks, die namentlich in den drei ersten Sätzen bald zu scharfen dramatischen Akzenten, bald zu besinnlichen Wendungen führt. Ganz anders das g moll-Quintett, „neben der g moll-Sinfonie das tiefsinnigste g moll-Stück Mozarts", das sich „ein- und derselben Stimmung, der schmerzlichsten Resignation mit einem Nachdruck hingibt, der erschütternd wirkt". Dieses Werk ist „der direkte Antipode der Klavierkonzerte, die Schöpfung eines Einsamen, der sich mit den dunkeln Schicksalsmächten auseinandersetzt, ohne ihrer im Beethovenschen Sinne Herr zu werden. Er nimmt sie mit allen Qualen, die sie ihm bereiten, als etwas Unabänderliches hin, und wenn er im Finale sich wieder der Lebensfreude zuwendet, so ist das nicht als Beethovenscher Sieg nach vorangegangenem Kampfe aufzufassen, sondern in Mozarts Sinne, der hier wieder einmal als Realist die entgegengesetzten Seiten der Wirklichkeit unmittelbar aneinanderrückt".[1])

Weniger bekannt als diese beiden Eckpfeiler der Quintettliteratur, aber darum nicht minder bedeutend, sind die beiden letzten Streichquintette in D dur (K. V. 593) vom Dezember 1790 und Es dur (K. V. 614) vom April 1791. Besonders das letztere weist durch seine heitere Grundstimmung und die bisweilen unverfälscht volkstümliche Themenerfindung wieder auf den frühen Mozart zurück, dessen musizierfreudige

Beschwingtheit hier im Dunstkreis der Zauberflötenstimmung erscheint.

Den Streichquintetten im weiteren Sinne zuzuweisen sind neben diesen fünf Werken die Umarbeitungen zweier Bläserserenaden, der B dur-Serenade (K. V. 361)[2]) und vor allem der c moll-Serenade (K. V. 388). Daß bei der Umarbeitung in ein Streicherensemble manche rein klanglichen Feinheiten verlorengehen mußten, ist klar. Dies ist besonders bei dem B dur-Werk der Fall. Andererseits war offenbar Mozart bei der c moll-Serenade von dem richtigen Empfinden geleitet, daß es sich hier um keine Serenadenmusik mehr handelt, sondern um eine, das g moll-Quintett vorausahnende Kammermusik tiefsten Gepräges. Dieses Werk darf man daher in der Umbesetzung für Streicher ohne Bedenken den originalen Streichquintetten als ebenbürtig zur Seite stellen.

Die vorliegende Ausgabe des g moll-Quintetts stützt sich auf das Autograph, das sich im Besitz der Preuß. Staatsbibliothek Berlin befindet. Die Abweichungen gegenüber den gangbaren praktischen Ausgaben beschränken sich im wesentlichen auf Phrasierungsbezeichnungen. Jedoch ermöglichte die Durchsicht der Urschrift vor allem im letzten Satz die Richtigstellung einiger romantisierender Glätten (T. 59, 1. Bratsche; T. 186, 2. Violine), die nicht bedeutungslos sein dürften.[3])

Rudolf Gerber

---

[1]) H. Abert, Mozart. 2. Bd. S. 387.
[2]) Vgl. Eulenburg-Ausgabe Nr. 100.
[3]) Vgl. auch im ersten Satz T. 60/61 in der 1. Bratsche; T. 96, 2. Bratsche und T. 100, 2. Viol

Quintet

I

W. A. Mozart
1756-1791
Köchel · N⁰ 516

Allegro

Violino I
Violino II
Viola I
Viola II
Violoncello

   Ernst Eulenburg Ltd

18

Menuetto.
Allegretto.

II.

III.

Adagio ma non troppo.

attacca.

32